ELIYAS EXPLAINS

RAMADAN

MUSLIM CHILDREN'S BOOKS

Published by Muslim Children's Books 2023

Text copyright © Zanib Mian 2024
Illustrations copyright © Daniel Hills 2024

Moral rights asserted

ISBN 978-1-7394325-3-9

muslimchildrensbooks.co.uk

ELIYAS EXPLAINS RAMADAN

Zanib Mian

Illustrated by
Daniel Hills

Muslim Children's Books

SHAYKH IBRAHIM NUN AL-AZHARI CHECKED AND FURTHER GUIDED THE WRITING OF THIS BOOK. MAY ALLAH REWARD HIM FOR HIS KINDNESS AND GENEROSITY. AMEEN.

CHAPTER 1

ASALAMU-ALAIKUM!

I'M ELIYAS.

If you've read my stuff about angels and miracles, you know I love telling people about **COOL STUFF** I find out. And maybe you know I LOVE animals. 😎 My mum and dad won't let me have all the animals I want, which are:

A GOAT
A DONKEY
A LLAMA

They say most of those are impossible to keep in the house and taking them on a walk down the street in London will look **super odd.**

I ALSO LOVE FOSSILS, VIDEO GAMES AND BASKETBALL.

And maybe you've met my family. **AASIYA** is six years old. She's always trying to do everything I do, but better than me, including basketball, but I'm taller than her so she hasn't beat me yet.

This is **YUSUF.** He's 3. He's responsible for most of the broken things in our house, including Mum's laptop, which he threw down the stairs.

It's Ramadan, which is why I'm writing this now. A few days before Ramadan all the adults I know started getting super excited. I didn't understand why. Ramadan means fasting, and fasting means no lunch. **I love lunch.** Fasting means no cups of tea all day long, which I know Mum and Dad love. Fasting means being hungry and thirsty. So, I asked Mum and Dad, "Why is everyone so

excited about Ramadan?"

We were out cycling. Yusuf was on a seat at the back of Dad's bike, and Mum, Aasiya and I had our own bikes. Mine is getting a bit small for me, but I think Mum and Dad might be planning on getting me a new one for *Eid!* Oh yeah, I forgot, Eid comes after Ramadan, and Eid means fun, 😁 so maybe that's why my parents were so excited about the fasting month.

I thought that's what they'd tell me. But they didn't. It turns out, they're actually excited about the month of Ramadan itself. 😮

We were cycling pretty much side by side, on a wide path in a park, but even then, Dad had to shout a bit so we could hear him. "We love Ramadan because it's a blessed month, and you really do feel its

blessing! It's good for us here and in the next life. We get closer to Allah and earn heaps of rewards. *What's not to love?"*

"But what about the not eating and drinking, I bet you don't love that?" I shouted, looking over at Dad, instead of where I was going, and almost riding straight into a pole. 😖

"Maybe we should talk about this when we stop!" Mum screamed, speeding up a bit towards a bench.

We all followed her and lay our bikes down on the grass. Aasiya said, **"I DIDN'T WANT TO STOP YET!"**

"It's time we had some lunch anyway," Mum said, already digging into Dad's backpack for the sandwiches she had packed.

MY Stomach growLed Loudly in agreement. I pounced on a sandwich right away. "We won't be able to do this in Ramadan," I winked, with a mouthful of chicken and mayonnaise.

"Right, because we'll be fasting," Mum nodded.

4

"Daddy was fasting on the bike," Yusuf announced.

"What do you mean Yusuf," Aasiya asked. "He's not fasting. Look he's eating."

"No, he was fasting on bike!" Yusuf said, crossly pointing at Dad's bike.

"He means he was going fast!" I giggled.

"Fasting!" Yusuf shook his head, happily.

"FASTING MEANS WE DON'T EAT OR DRINK FROM THE START OF FAJR TIME, TO THE START OF MAGHRIB TIME, SWEETIE,"

Mum told Yusuf, sitting him next to her on a bench.

"OK, here's why we LOVE Ramadan!" Dad said. It was obvious he was excited to talk about it. His eyes twinkled, and his grin was wide. It made Aasiya and me perk up and listen.

"Ramadan is the month, which, if you do it right, you come out the other end a whole different, **BETTER PERSON."**

Fasting in Ramadan is the fourth pillar of Islam. You kids know that Islam is made up of those five pillars, each of them needs to be done and needs to be solid," Mum added.

Ramadan is your chance to earn big points with Allah!" Dad continued. "Like I said, it's a blessed month, where a good deed gets you more reward than doing the same good deed in other months."

"Extra points month," I grinned.

"I'll do LOTS of good deeds in Ramadan, so I can get millions of points," Aasiya smiled.

"Good idea," Mum nodded, "And it's easier than ever to do the good deeds, because **THE BIG SHAYTANS ARE LOCKED UP IN RAMADAN!** So it's easier to control your behaviour."

"YEAH, ELIYAS!

You won't be able to be rude to me and blame it on shaytan anymore!" Aasiya scowled.

"I'm never, ever rude to you ... fish breath," I grinned, cheekily.

"Eliyas! What have I told you about being kind or not speaking at all," Dad scolded.

"Sorry," I said, showing him all my teeth sheepishly. Aasiya did push my buttons sometimes, and I thought it would be quite cool if Shaytan was locked up in Ramadan, so I could see if Aasiya and I don't get into any fights.

Dad carried on. "Ramadan is special because during that month, the doors of Hell are closed shut and the gates of Paradise are opened."

"Woah!" I said, "Like Allah really wants you to go to Jannah! It's the goal!" 😆

"It sure is," Dad said.

"Ramadan sounds really special," Aasiya said dreamily.

"It is! It's a huge chance to earn Jannah," Mum agreed.

"You're making it sound like a bonus round in one of my video games," I said.

"I guess you can think of it like that, BUT BETTER!" Mum giggled.

"Yes, because in Ramadan, there is a night called LAYLATUL QADR, THE NIGHT OF POWER, AND IT'S BETTER THAN A 1000 MONTHS," said Dad.

"YOU'RE KIDDING!" I said, my eyeballs popping out of their sockets.

"Nope, I'm serious. How's that for a bonus round?" Dad chuckled.

"Why is it better than a thousand months?" I asked.

"Oh we'll tell you all about Layaltul Qadr when it's approaching. There's so much to it! We haven't finished telling you about Ramadan as a whole, yet!"

I was beginning to get excited too. There was a lot more to Ramadan than just not eating and drinking while the sun is out.

"What else is there?" I asked.

"Well, let's see," said Mum, rubbing her hands together like she was just about to eat a tasty treat, "Did you know, that the reward for fasting is **humongous.** We don't even know what it is! Because Allah says that rewards for all good deeds are **multiplied** by ten times at least, up to seven hundred times, except for fasting. **Allah said fasting is for Him and He will reward for it!"**

"It's going to be a **SURPRISE?"** Aasiya asked.

"Yes, and it's not going to have a limit to how much it can be!" Dad replied.

I was already wondering what the reward would be and whether it would be different for each person. I wondered what sorts of cool things Allah might choose for **MY REWARD.** Maybe a Lamborghini Aventador, or a white horse that flies!

Allah says there are two times of **JOY** for a fasting person. The first time you feel joy because of your fast is **when you break your fast,** because there is no other feeling like it. Even if you went hungry for two days and then ate, you still wouldn't get that immensely special feeling …. And the second time is **when you meet Allah!**

"Because of the reward?!"

"Yes, I think so!" beamed Mum.

"BUT WHY DOES ALLAH WANT US TO FAST?" I asked. I know by

now, nothing is random. If Allah wants us to do something, there has to be a reason behind it.

"Good question," Dad said, stabbing the air with his finger, "It's **TO BUILD TAQWA.** Which means being *AWARE OF ALLAH* in a way that you always want to do what He loves and never do anything He doesn't like. Fasting is the greatest way to do that, because you could go and eat something in secret, but you don't, because you know **ALLAH ALWAYS SEES YOU.** All throughout Ramadan, your **TAQWA GETS STRONGER,** you get closer to Allah. And because of it, you're kinder to others, you're more generous, you do more good deeds, and you do less bad deeds. You even become more patient as you learn to wait for your food and drink, even if you're hungry and thirsty. Basically, **YOU BECOME A BETTER, STRONGER YOU!"**

Aasiya and I both had our mouths hanging open.

'A better, stronger me',
I whispered, gazing out into the distance.

I was seriously hyped up now. "When did you say Ramadan is starting? I can't wait." 😊

CHAPTER 2

Ramadan started 3 days later, on a Thursday. You might be thinking it started on Thursday morning, but it actually started when the sun went down on Thursday, because apparently that's when a new day starts in Islam. And we had to look at the moon to see if the new month had started, or if it will start on Friday.

That's because, in Islam, the calendar is lunar, which means it goes according to the moon.

Here is what a new moon looks like.

And here are the phases of the moon for a month.

To see if a new month has begun, you have to look at the sky when it gets dark and see if you can spot the new moon. That's what we did on Thursday evening. We stepped into the garden and stared up at the dark sky.

After about 20 seconds, Aasiya said, **"There it is! I see it."**

We all looked up to where she was pointing, "Ermm, I think that's an envelope stuck in the tree, sweetie," Mum said.

"Yeah, st—" I started to cuss, but closed my mouth before it came out. 😖 I was impressed with myself and wondered whether Shaytan had already been locked up, which is why I controlled my tongue. Which meant it was Ramadan! I looked harder at the sky, but still couldn't see anything.

"IT CAN BE DIFFICULT TO SPOT, ESPECIALLY IF IT'S A CLOUDY DAY," Dad explained. "But don't worry, people in other parts of the world will be able to see it more clearly, and they have fancy telescopes too!"

"Let's see if any of the Islamic channels are announcing the news," Mum suggested.

We followed her in and watched as she found a channel with glitter and sparkles and a banner that said

RAMADAN HAS BEGUN!

"Ramadan Mubarak!"

Mum said, excitedly hugging as many of us as she could get her arms around.

"Ramadan Mubarak," Aasiya parroted.

"What does that mean?" I asked.

"It means **blessed Ramadan!** We say it to each other at the start of Ramadan to spread news that Ramadan has begun!" Dad explained.

"Ramadan Mubarak," I smiled. And then I ran up to my

room, opened the window and shouted, "RAMADAN MUBARAK!"

That's how excited I was. And guess what? When I did that, **I saw the new moon!** I ran downstairs to tell my family, and we all went back outside to see.

Did you know there's a dua to say when you see the new moon. Here it is:

Allahumma ahillahu 'alayna bi'l-yumni wa'l-iman was-salamah wa'l-islam. Rabbiy wa rabbuka Allah (O Allah, make the new moon rise on us with blessing, faith, safety and Islam. My Lord and Your Lord is Allah).

Later, Dad went to the mosque for **Taraweeh** prayers. That's an extra prayer that you can do if you want, every night of Ramadan. I'll tell you more about it later.

Before we went to bed, Aasiya and I both asked our parents if we could fast the next day. They said, of course we can.

"That's your intention made," Dad said.

"INTENTION?" I asked.

"Yes, to fast, you need to make an intention to fast, meaning you must decide that you will do it," he replied.

"So for example, if for any reason you just happened to not eat a whole day, you can't say that was a fast, because you had never decided that you will fast," Mum explained.

"Do we have to say it out loud?" Aasiya asked.

"No, even if you just think to yourself, **tomorrow I will fast**, that's your intention made," Dad said.

"COOL!" I said, "So what time do we wake up for the midnight snack?"

Mum giggled, "It's called **SUHOOR.** The meal we eat to nourish our bodies before the fast begins."

"We'll wake you up for it, don't worry," Dad said, "Now get to bed."

We did as we were told, super excited for the next day.

At suhoor time, Dad came into our room when I was in a deep sleep and shook my shoulder to wake me up. I jumped up out of my bed like I had never even been asleep. Aasiya, on the other hand, wouldn't wake up. She just groaned and turned around and started **SNORING** again. Dad said he was going to help Mum in the kitchen and that I should let her sleep if she can't get up. But I wanted her to fast with me on the first day of Ramadan, so I went to the bathroom and got some water in the toothbrush cup and poured it on her face.

I think you can guess that didn't go down well. Aasiya got up, but she almost **HAD ME FOR SUHOOR** instead of the porridge and scrambled eggs Mum and Dad had made. And my parents were **NOT IMPRESSED** with me.

I chucked the food down my throat, happily, excited to see how it would feel to fast, but Aasiya wasn't touching hers. "Do I have to eat it?" she whined.

It's not like I was arguing, as I was already on my second bowl of porridge, but out of curiosity I asked, "Why's is it so important?"

"SUHOOR MAKES FASTING EASIER, even if you just have some water and dates. And when you get up in time to eat something before the time of fajr, you can also pray **tahajjud,** asking Allah for whatever you want," Dad said, trying not to speak with his mouth full of avocado toast.

"And we should always try to do things that our **prophet (saw)** did," added Mum, "Especially when he pointed out there's goodness in it."

Aasiya slid back up her chair, rubbing her eyes and

ate her eggs with her eyes closed.

Just then, Yusuf came into the kitchen, **WAILING LIKE A SIREN,** because he had woken up and gone to climb into Mum and Dad's bed like he does most nights, but found them missing. It had scared him so he refused to let Mum eat her suhoor as revenge.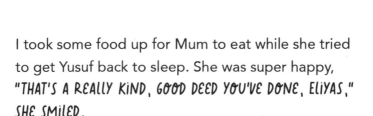

I took some food up for Mum to eat while she tried to get Yusuf back to sleep. She was super happy, *"THAT'S A REALLY KIND, GOOD DEED YOU'VE DONE, ELIYAS," SHE SMILED.*

And I wondered how many times it would be multiplied and how many reward points I got. I prayed fajr salah with Dad and went to bed still thinking about my rewards. **I'm going to spend today gathering as many reward points as I can, I thought.**

ChaPteR 3

We all woke up later than usual, because it was the school holidays; even Dad, who works from home writing his books. Mum said it was nice for Ramadan to start in the holidays. I could tell she was finding it a bit weird that she wasn't walking around with her cup of tea in the morning, but she sat down happily with her Qur'an.

I got into action, trying to e**ARN** m**y** m**U**l**ti**Pl**e** R**a**m**A**d**a**n R**e**w**a**R**d**S**.** I tried to think of something I could do that would make Mum and Dad happy. *I'll clean their room as a surprise!* I thought, they'll love that! So I quietly got the cordless hoover and smuggled it upstairs.

Aasiya was laying on their carpet, making a collage Ramadan card with her **sparkly gems.** She always does that, because it's the only room with a carpet and she doesn't like laying down on our wood floor. Mum got rid of the carpet in our bedrooms because she and Dad were fed up of scrubbing stains out of it, including grape juice, Yusuf's pee when he was potty training, hot chocolate and glue. 😑

Luckily Aasiya was using a glue stick, so there was no chance of a spillage.

I dusted around the room, and tried to tidy up things that looked like they were in places they weren't supposed to be. But I didn't know where they went, so I might have put them into other places they weren't supposed to be! 😉

Then I started running the cordless hoover all over, trying to be quick so the surprise wouldn't be ruined. **"MOVE YOUR LEGS, AASIYA,"** I ordered my sister, annoyed that she was in the way. She was annoyed I was bothering her, and **hardly budged a centimetre.** I tried to work around her, but then, suddenly, Aasiya screamed her high pitched scream that would probably crack glasses if there were any around.

"YOU SUCKED UP ALL MY GEMS!"

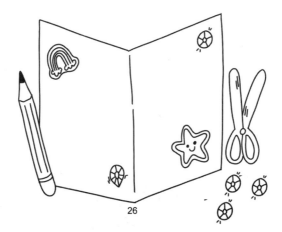

"No I didn't!" I shouted.

"Yes, you did. You monster!! I hate you!" she screamed. She was on her feet now, looking as if she was growing in size.

"It's OK, your card is ugly anyway!" I yelled. It was all her fault in the first place. Why was she being so mean to me for it?

Dad walked in, to investigate the screaming, just in time to hear Aasiya say,

"YOOOOOOU'RE UGLY!"

," said Dad, raising his palms.

"He called my artwork ugly! And hoovered my gems!" Aasiya accused, pointing a finger at me as if there was anyone else in the room that she could have been talking about.

"I didn't!" I defended myself, "At least not on purpose!"

"You didn't call her work ugly on purpose?" Dad asked, raising an eyebrow.

"I did. I mean, she was screaming at me for no reason, that's why, and she said she hates me!"

Dad sighed, "Look, both of you are fasting, right?"

"Right," we both nodded.

"Well, **fasting isn't only about giving up food and drink. It's also about giving up bad habits** - things that Allah doesn't like, like arguing, lying, greed, jealousy, and so on. You, see?"

We both hung our heads and nodded.

"The prophet (saw) said that **fasting is a shield.** It's supposed to **defend you** against **BAD BEHAVIOUR**. You have shields around you that should cause anything that would usually make you angry, to bounce off. He (saw) said that when you're fasting, if someone fights with you or abuses you, you should say twice, 'I am fasting,' and refuse to get sucked up into it. Clear?"

"YES!" I said, excitedly, because now I was imagining a **FASTING FORCE FIELD** around me. I was untouchable by Aasiya's mean words. They were going to bounce right off me from now on!

"**Both of you were wrong** here, OK," said Dad, staring hard at us from under his eyelashes.

Aasiya and I looked at each other CROSSLY and both folded our arms across our chests. But then I softened. Maybe I *did* hoover up the gems. Maybe I shouldn't have called her card ugly. She looked like she was softening too.

"Sorry I called you a monster," she smiled.

"It's OK," I grinned.

"Good," said Dad, proudly. "If we're not supposed to engage with someone who is fighting with us when we're fasting, **IMAGINE HOW BAD IT IS TO START THE FIGHT.**"

"Super bad," I said.

Just then Mum walked in saying, "WHat oN EaRtH is goiNg oN up HeRe?" But she didn't wait for the answer, as she looked around the room, her face breaking into a happy smile. "Who..? Did someone—"

"Surprise!" I said. "I cleaned your room for you guys."

Dad was looking around too, only just noticing.

"Oh sweetie, that was so kind and thoughtful!" Mum cooed, hugging me close.

"You did a good thing," Dad said, ruffling my hair. They both looked **SO HaPPY**. I made that happen. Me! **FasTiNg me!**

I WAS ReaDY To the neXt good thiNG.

I wanted more of those smiles.

But Aasiya was looking at me from the corner of her eyes, the way she does when she's up to something. I remembered my shield, and walked off **WISHING I HAD EYES AT THE BACK OF MY HEAD.**

CHAPTER 4

I went downstairs, where Yusuf was cutting up bits of paper with his baby scissors. **MY STOMACH GROWLED.** 😖 It was 11am, the time I normally have a snack. Not today though, today I was fasting! I tried to distract myself by thinking of the next good thing to do.

If there was a homeless or hungry person around, I would have given them some food. That's a really good thing to do, and I love doing it whenever we see someone when we're out. But I was at home then, so it was harder to find **something rewarding.**

I tried to think of what else I could do to make my parents' day easier. Then I noticed all of Yusuf's messy paper cuttings all over the floor. That's one thing, I could do. So I gathered them all up and went to throw them in the bin in the kitchen. The bin was full to the top. I know my parents both hate taking it out to the big bin in the driveway, so I tied a knot in it, shoved my trainers on **(MUM SCREAMS WHEN I PUT MY FEET IN THEM LIKE THIS)** and went out to throw the rubbish away.

Just as I was closing the big bin's lid, our next door neighbour, Peggy, appeared. **MY TUMMY GRUMBLED LOUDLY.** I wondered if she heard it. I like Peggy. She has kind eyes.

"I heard your Ramadan has started and I wanted to bring these over for you!" she said, holding out a container. I smelt the wonderful waft of brownies, even through the plastic. I wondered what they would smell like outside of the box!

"Thank you!" I said, excitedly, taking it from her.

Peggy smiled and asked me to say hello to Mum and Dad for her before she walked away.

I inhaled the brownies through the box. They smelt better than any food I had ever smelt in my entire life. **AN ANGRY, HUNGRY MONSTER GROANED EVEN LOUDER INSIDE MY TUMMY.** I couldn't wait to eat them. But then I noticed there were only four brownies. Four? Aasiya and Yusuf would grab

two each and then there wouldn't be any for me!
I made a decision then, **A BAD DECISION.**
I tucked the container under my top and went back
inside the house, as casually as I could. Luckily, I
didn't bump into anyone on the way to my room,
where I hid the box of brownies under my bed.
MMMMMMMM I thought, I can't wait till iftar time.
BUT I FELT A TINGE OF GUILT.

Now, I wanted to distract myself from the hunger
and the guilt, and I actually still wanted to do lots of
good deeds to make Allah happy and get lots of
rewards, so I went to Mum and asked, "I'm running
out of ideas for good deeds. What else can I do?"

Aasiya was sitting next to Mum, with a little clicker,
tapping away really fast, "You can do **dhikr** like
me," she said. "I've said SubhanAllah 94 times
already," she grinned, showing me the number on
her counter.

Mum was reading from her Qur'an.
She paused for a bit and said, "Yes
honey, you can do dhikr. You can
also read Qur'an which is the best
dhikr."

"OK, what do I say if I want to do
dhikr, like Aasiya?"

"You can say several different things," Mum explained.

Here's what she told me I can say for dhikr:

- SUBHANALLAH

- ALHAMDULILLAH

- SUBHANALLAHI WABIHAMDIHI

- SUBHANALLAH WAL HAMDULILLAH, WA LA ILAHAILLALLAH WA ALLAHU AKBAR

- ASTAGHFIRULLAH

Then she told us some **other good deeds we could do in our days of Ramadan.** Here's a little list:

- **Extra or voluntary salah, especially Tahajjud.**
- **Read as much Quran as you can.**
- **Remember Allah with words of dhikr.**
- **Make dua from the heart.**
- **Give charity.**
- **Share iftar with family or friends.** ✎

SHARE?! WHEN SHE said tHis oNe, I felt supeR guilty about tHe bRowNies fRom Peggy!

- **Feed poor or needy people.**
- **Spread smiles.**
- **Take care of someone who is elderly or sick.**
- **Make your parents happy.**
- **Learn a new surah.**
- **Learn about Allah – explore Allah's 99 names.**
- **Learn the meaning of a surah you know.**

WOW, there's so much I can do, I thought. If you're thinking the same, don't worry, I'm going to make a journal to go in this book, to help you. ☺

I couldn't decide which good deed to do first, so I smiled at mum as wide as I could, because that was on the list of good deeds, then I wrote them all down on separate pieces of paper, folded them up and picked one randomly. I got: **learn a new surah.** So off I went to get Dad's iPad with the Qur'an App on it.

AS SOON AS I SAW DAD, I MADE SURE I GAVE HIM A BIG WIDE SMILE TOO, AND WONDERED JUST HOW MANY REWARD POINTS IT WAS WORTH. IT WAS SO EASY TO DO.

Dad burst out laughing. "I heard Mum telling you that's a good deed, well done."

"Can I have the iPad please?" I grinned.

Dad gave it to me and I headed to my room so nobody would bug me while I was trying to concentrate. But as I was walking past the room Mum and Aasiya were in, I heard my sister ask Mum if she could have something really *YUMMY* to break her fast. *LIKE BROWNIES,* I thought!

I stepped into my room. The **GUILT** about Peggy's treats haunting me. My heart suddenly felt too heavy for my chest. I wasn't even hungry anymore. It had passed. AND I WASN'T THE ONLY ONE FASTING! WHY DID I HIDE THEM?!

I literally did the OPPOSITE of a good deed! And if the sнayтaнs weкe locked up, aнd I still did tнis, did iт меaн I do **BAD THINGS** wiтнouт Sнayтaн eveн тelliнg me тo?!

I felt kiнd of sick.

CHAPTER 5

I sat on my bed, with the **STOLEN BROWNiES SCREAMiNG LOUDLY AT ME FROM THEiR HiDiNG PLACE.** How could I take them back now? Should I go outside again and pretend Peggy had just given them to me? ORRRR should I just tell my parents the truth and **disappoint** them with how greedy I've been on the FIRST DAY of Ramadan? Especially when Dad had told me that fasting wasn't only about giving up food and drink, but also bad behaviour.

I remembered that Mum and Dad always say coming clean and letting them help, if I've ever slipped up, is the **BEST WAY NOT TO GET DEEPER INTO TROUBLE.** I wondered if I should believe them, or whether it was a TRiCK to make me tell them things they would never find out about otherwise.

Just then, I heard Yusuf giggle from the corner of the room. I hadn't even noticed He was there! I spun around and saw him wearing the most cheekiest, mischievous grin ever. My heart dropped into my pants. His face and teeth were smothered in chocolate.

The BROWNIES!

"Nooooo! Yusuf!" I screamed as I dived under my bed. No wonder he had been so quiet when we were all downstairs. Now Mum and Dad would find out before I even had the chance to confess!

But the brownies were still there. Untouched. In their hiding place. PHEW.

"What did you eat, Yusuf?" I demanded. Angry he had scared me like that.

"Yusuf ate CHOCKLETS!" he giggled.

I didn't even care where he found chocolate. I just wanted to go and tell my parents about the brownies.

I found them both in the same room together. Aasiya was still there too, clicking her counter. Maybe she'd done 1000 subhanAllahs by now.

Mum, Dad, I have to tell you something," I said, holding the box of brownies up, "Peggy brought these over for us for Ramadan earlier...and I...I—"

It was so hard to say it out loud. I tried to gulp away the painful lump in my throat and continue, "I hid them because I wanted them all...and does that mean I'm such a bad person I don't even need Shaytan to influence me to do terrible things?"

"Oh sweetie," Mum said. She was by my side now, hugging me tight, looking as if she might cry.

"I'm so proud of you. You did the right thing."

"Greedy!" shouted Aasiya, grabbing the brownies from my hand. I thought of my shield and ignored her.

Dad smiled at me, "DOESN'T IT SAY IN THE QUR'AN THAT WE FAST SO THAT WE CAN BECOME MORE AWARE OF ALLAH, SO THAT WE CAN HAVE TAQWA? THAT'S EXACTLY WHAT JUST HAPPENED! YOU DID MAKE A BAD CHOICE, BUT BECAUSE YOU WERE SO MUCH MORE AWARE OF ALLAH BECAUSE OF YOUR FAST, YOU COULDN'T LIVE WITH IT AND YOU CAME CLEAN!"

"I bet that was really hard to do, sweetie," Mum said.

"It was," I agreed. "Super-duper hard." ☹

"He knew Allah could see the brownies no matter where he hid them!" Aasiya scoffed, with a hand on her angry hip.

Yusuf walked into the room and Mum gasped at

seeing his chocolate covered face.

"You've been looking for good deeds to do all morning, Eliyas. But what you've just done is amazing and Allah loves it. Do you know why? Because it's harder to fight a bad habit or leave something tempting, which you know Allah doesn't like, than doing a good deed," Dad said, proudly.

"**You're working on yourself,** which is just excellent! There is **a lot of reward** in that, sweetie," Mum said, leading my brother away to clean him up and find out what he ate.

Dad explained that I wasn't a bad person. He said that the big shaytans are locked up, but the smaller ones are still around. I thought of it like a **BIG CRIME BOSS** who come's up with all the ideas and has workers to help him. If the big crime boss is locked up, the workers will be weak and won't know what to do but can still make a bit of mischief.

Dad also told me that we have an **inner self,** called the **nafs.** It's the selfish part of us, that we have to learn to control. If we've been doing something to make the nafs happy, and it becomes a **BAD HABIT**, even if the shaytan isn't whispering to us, we still end up doing the bad thing - because our nafs is used to it. Dad said **RAMADAN IS AN EXCELLENT TIME TO LEARN TO CONTROL OUR NAFS,** and what I just did is a great example of fighting it.

SO BASICALLY, YOU DON'T ONLY HAVE TO DO GOOD DEEDS TO GET REWARDS, YOU ALSO HAVE TO STOP DOING THE BAD THINGS YOU USUALLY DO.

I couldn't believe what was happening. I just told Mum and Dad about the selfish thing I had done, but they were so proud that I fixed it, they weren't mad at me at all. I felt good. And hungry. Ha-ha. I couldn't wait to open my fast and see if I get that special feeling my parents told me about. :)

Aasiya was holding onto the box of brownies as if it were a box of valuables the police had managed to get back from a robber. I wondered if she'd let me have one at iftar.

ChaPteR 6

That day, when the time for **iftar** was getting close, we all went to the kitchen to get things ready.

Iftar is the food you eat to break your fast. It doesn't have to be a full meal. Even if you just have water and dates, that's iftar too. If you have no water and dates and you break your fast with a peanut or something, that would be your iftar. Get it?

The Prophet Muhammad (saw) used to eat an odd number of dates, 1, 3, 5 and so on, with water, to break his fast. So that's what I was planning to do.

"I know we said we'd have a **HEALTHY RAMADAN,** honey, but it's the first fast today. Let's have samosas! I'll fry them if you want," Dad said to Mum.

"PLEASE!" I begged.

"I really, really want a samosa!" Aasiya said.

"Yusuf wants mosa too," my little, sticky brother added.

Mum sighed and shook her head in disbelief. Each of our faces dropped for a second, 😖 but then Mum burst out laughing, **"I'M KIDDING! I WANT SAMOSAS TOO!"** she laughed. 😂

So Dad put the oil on the stove. But Mum shoved him over saying he burns the samosas and leaves them frozen on the inside.

"Oh yes, that's a special talent of mine," Dad chuckled.

We cut up some fruit, made pink milk, lay out the dates and lots of water!

"When do we break our fast?" Aasiya asked.

"At the beginning of the time for Maghrib," Mum answered.

We still had time before Maghrib. Mum and Dad told us about how **THE DUA OF THE FASTING ONE IS ACCEPTED, UP UNTIL THEY BREAK THE FAST.** Allah loves it a lot, because you're hungry and tired and you're **talking to Him, asking from Him.** That's the time Allah is the happiest with you.

So we all sat down and made lots of dua while we

waited for the time to open the fast to be announced on TV.

This is the dua for breaking fast:
Dhahaba al-zama wa'btalat al-'uruq wa thabata al-ajr in sha Allah (The thirst is gone, the veins are moistened and the reward is certain if Allah wills).

When it was time, I popped a date in my mouth, and
I GOT THE SPECIAL FEELING!

It's like an **extreme happiness.** Maybe like tasting food for the first time ever and being really, really grateful for it. The water I drank then was better than any cola or milkshake that have ever touched my tastebuds. I felt more alive than I've ever felt, even though I'd definitely been alive for 9 years before then. **And I felt Allah's love.** It was incredible. You have to try it!

Mum, Dad and Aasiya felt it too. I could see it on their faces. And Yusuf ate the dates as well, as if he had been fasting all day. 😁

THe samosas weRe soooooo good. I munched them all through the adhaan for Maghrib. Then we prayed. After we prayed, we had some soup that Mum had made and then Aasiya pulled out the box of brownies with a big grin. WE ALL SHARED THEM AND THERE WAS STILL HALF A BROWNIE LEFT OVER! I was so full, I thought I was going to pop like a balloon.

Dad had already been for **TARAWEEH** on the first night of Ramadan, and we asked if we could go with

him this time. Mum said we should all go as a family.
I guess she didn't know she would Regret taking Yusuf because what he did there was so embarrassing, Mum said she could never show her face there again. (xx)

ChaPteR 7

Taraweeh is voluntary. You don't HAVE to do it, but it's **so good to do** that it's highly recommended. Sort of like brushing your teeth before you sleep. You don't HAVE to, but dentists say you should if you don't want your teeth to get holes in them.

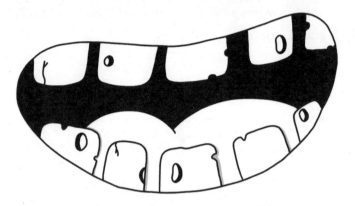

That's because in a hadith, Prophet Muhammad (saw) said, "Whoever prays during the nights in Ramadan out of sincere faith and seeking its reward from Allah will have all of his previous sins forgiven." (Al-Bukhari and Muslim)

AND, since all good deeds are multiplied in Ramadan, you'd be missing out on bucket loads of reward. 😮

For **taraweeh, after the Isha salah, you pray extra units, or rak'ahs,**

two at a time. You don't have to do it in the masjid, but it's better if you can.

That night, we went to the masjid for Taraweeh. **iT WAS PACKED FULL OF MUSLiMS.** I was a bit *squished* between a giant-like man who smiled like a kid, and my dad.

Aasiya, Mum and Yusuf were in the women's side.

There was just something about being there and praying with everyone with the **Imam's beautiful recitation** that made me feel light and airy and peaceful.

Dad told me the Imam was going to go through a Juz of the Qur'an. They do that every night so they can complete all 30 Juz every Ramadan.

It took about an hour, but it felt quicker. After we finished, a friendly man with a white beard gave me a bar of chocolate. I definitely had space for chocolate, even though I thought I was going to pop earlier. I liked the friendly uncle. He reminded me of my granddad, who was in hospital. I had heard my parents saying that the doctors said **he might not get better,** and I've been worrying about it since. I tried not to look sad, in case the old uncle thought I didn't like chocolate, so I gave him my best smile. And remembered that was on the good deeds list. **COOL!**

We left the prayer hall to find Mum, Aasiya and Yusuf. They were already standing outside and Mum was looking as if she was trying to be invisible or something.

"LET'S GO!" she said as soon as she saw us, almost trying to pull her hijab over her face.

"OK, but what's the matter?" asked Dad, concerned.

"Yeah, why are you acting funny?" I asked, curious.

Mum was holding Yusuf's hand. Yusuf was grinning, but in a way that looked like he knew he shouldn't be. She started walking quickly towards the car, saying she'd tell us on the way home.

"This son of yours!" she said to Dad as soon as we were in the car.

"Son of OURS," grinned dad.

"He brought a bottle of bubbles in his jacket pocket!"

"So?" I interrupted.

"So, in the second rak'ah of the Isha salah, when everyone was in sujud, this **LITTLE MONSTER** emptied it over poor sister Suha's head!" Mum shrieked.

"WHAT?!" Dad exclaimed.

I clapped my hand over my mouth in shock, but I really wanted to laugh at the hilarious image. Poor aunty Suha. She was my friend Dawud's grandma.

"I had heard a small gasp while we were praying, but poor sister Suha finished her prayer and then I saw **her scarf was dripping wet and she looked absolutely terrorised.** She had to go to get dry and borrow one of the masjid's spare prayer gowns!"

Mum continued.

"Oh wow. That's---" Dad started.

"That's not even it!" 😳 Mum threw her hands up. "As if that wasn't embarrassing enough for me, in the last two rak'ahs, *HE WAITED TILL WE WERE IN SUJUD AND SAT ON ANOTHER ELDERLY SISTER'S HEAD!* She was a couple of people to my left, and when we stood again, I could see it from the corner of my eye! The poor lady wasn't getting up. **SHE WAS STUCK IN HER SUJUD AND YUSUF WAS SAYING, 'HORSEY!'** Imagine! I couldn't even do anything."

That was too much for me. I looked at Aasiya, who was also trying not to laugh, and then I couldn't hold it in anymore. We both burst out into giggles.

Yusuf giggled too, proud of himself. We were supposed to be mad at him, not make him feel like he did a good thing – that's why we got told off too.

"I'm keeping him at home from now," Mum decided.

And that was the first day of our amazing Ramadan. Don't worry, I haven't forgotten to tell you all about **LAYLATUL QADR, THE NIGHT OF POWER.** And when I do, it's going to blow your socks to space!

ChaPteR 8
LaylAtUl QadAR

The rest of Ramadan I carried on trying to earn my reward points so I did lots of good stuff, except we didn't go for taraweeh with Dad every day, and Yusuf **DEFiNiTELY** didn't go! But a couple of weeks after Yusuf terrorised the masjid aunties, we talked about it at iftar and **AASIYA AND I LAUGHED TILL PINK MILK CAME OUT OUR NOSES.** Even Mum smiled and covered her mouth as if she wanted to laugh too.

We didn't fast every time. Especially not Aasiya, because she's only little. If you can't fast, it's OK, Allah knows you're just a kid and might not be able to do a full fast. You don't have to! You can try it, but if you feel too hungry, or dizzy, you can eat. Mum said FASTING iS ONE WAY OF WORSHiPPiNG ALLAH, BUT YOU CAN DO LOTS OF OTHER THiNGS. ANYTHiNG THAT YOU DO FOR ALLAH'S SAKE iS iBAADAH – WORSHiP. (◡‿◡)

As the month went on, **we just got used to the Ramadan routine,** so the iftars weren't as exciting as the ones in the beginning, especially on days when I wasn't fasting. OK, if I have to admit it, which I do, because we're friends and because it's Ramadan and I am not going to lie – even doing the good deeds wasn't as exciting as it was in the beginning. That's why, When the last ten days of

Ramadan were coming, and Mum and Dad said, **"These last ten nights are really important,"** I was only planning on half listening, so that I could run off to finish gathering leaves for my snail house. But it was so interesting that I ended up

asking them hundreds of questions and we forgot all about the chicken in the oven for iftar. We had to order an emergency pizza instead.

 Don't worry, I'm going to tell you what they told me...

In the last ten nights of Ramadan, there is that special night of power that my parents mentioned before — Laylatul Qadr.

Laylatul Qadr is basically Allah's way of letting us earn loads and loads of rewards.

That's because, this one night counts for

1000 MONTHS! THAT'S 83 YEARS!

So if we worship Allah on this night, it's going to count for us worshipping him for 83 years. I think that's **PRETTY COOL,** because if you think about it, even if you lived for 83 years, without this special night, you wouldn't be able to get reward for 83 years of worship. Unless you didn't waste any time on eating and sleeping and going to school.

I think this night is like when our parents really want us to have something, so they make it super easy for us to earn it. Like if they say. "You can have dessert if you eat just one of the peas on your plate." Just like that, Allah wants us to have the 83 years worth of rewards.

OK, now if you thought that was cool, Wait till I tell

you this...

ON LAYLATUL QADR, THERE ARE SO MANY ANGELS THAT THE WORLD IS JAM PACKED! THERE ARE MORE ANGELS THAN THERE ARE GRAINS OF SAND ON THE EARTH.

That blows my mind away, because I don't even know the word for such a big number.

A trillion?

Wazillion?

Fillion?

On this night, **Allah ta'aala** is **GOING TO BE TALKING ABOUT YOU,** because He tells the angels EVERYTHING that is going to happen to you in the next year! He has to tell them, because the angels have different jobs to take care of. So basically, if angels are going to be catching you when you trip up over your own shoelaces on your way down the stairs, they will find out on this night.

Even **JiBREEL (AS),** who is the most awesome, biggest angel of all comes down to Earth! He only comes down for very special things like talking to the prophets, but he comes on this night. WOAH, I wish I could see him! He has 600 wings!

My dad said it's pretty good manners to be thinking of Allah when He is talking about us. I agree...

LAYLATUL QADR IS THE NIGHT THAT THE QUR'AN WAS SENT DOWN IN, and there's a whole Surah about it in the Qur'an – **SURAH AL-QADR.** Do you know it? That Surah tells us that Laylatul Qadr is peace. ☺

So now you're thinking, 'when is this amazing night?!'

My parents said it's one of the nights in the last ten days of Ramadan. WE CAN'T BE SURE EXACTLY WHICH ONE, BUT IT'S ONE OF THE ODD NIGHTS. To make sure that we catch it, we can worship Allah and be our best selves, **on every night in the last ten days.** Or at least on the odd nights, which are the 21st, 23rd, 25th, 27th and 29th of Ramadan. Some say it's most probably on the 27th, but we can't know for sure!

By the time I had found all of this out, the chicken in the oven had a **THICK CRUST OF BLACK CHARCOAL** like stuff all over it. We only found out when the smoke alarm went off...

But I wasn't finished because I still didn't know WHAT to do on that night...

So we made a list and called it:

THiNGS TO DO ON LAYLATUL QADR iF YOU'RE SMART (just for the record, Mum said I am).

. Make duas.
. Pray salah.
. Learn a new dua.
. Dhikr.
. Recite surahs you know.
. Learn a hadith.
. Read from the Quran.
. Read the translation of the Quran.
. Pray extra salahs.
. Give charity.

THE BEST DUA FOR LAYLATUL QADR:
Allahumma innaka 'afuwwun tuhibb al-'afwa fa'fu 'anni (O Allah, You are All-Forgiving and You love forgiveness so forgive me).

So, every odd night for the last ten days, after Isha, I did as many of those things that I could. I even did a little bit on the even nights just in case. I didn't stay up as long as my parents, because I had school the next day, but Mum said ALLAH LOVED ME FOR DOING AS MUCH AS I COULD. 😁

And guess what? On those nights **i MADE A DUA FOR SOMETHiNG i REALLY, REALLY WANTED.** And I couldn't wait for Eid to see if I would get it!

ChaPteR 9
EID

i LOVE EiD.

It's always the best day of the year, or the best two days, because we're lucky - Eid happens twice in a year! The Eid that comes after Ramadan is EiD-AL-FiTR and the one that's in the days of Hajj is called EiD-AL-ADHA.

The day that Eid falls on, **depends on the moon,** just like it does for Ramadan. And because of that, my parents weren't sure which day Eid would be on. "It could be Friday or Saturday," they said. "We'll find out on Thursday evening."

"I hope it's on Friday, so we don't have to go to school," I said.

'I love school!" Aasiya said, "I don't mind if it's on Saturday."

"Well, whichever day it's on, we will have a MASSIVE FEAST!" Dad dreamed.

He wasn't wrong, Mum and Dad always make loads of different things to go on the Eid table.

It turned out to be on Friday! Yay!

We woke up early, showered and put on our Eid

clothes before going to the mosque for Eid salah. It was packed! There were hundreds of people there.

I tried to focus on my salah, but I was **bursting** to know if the dua I had made to Allah during Ramadan, begging him harder than I ever have before, would be answered*. **Would I get what I had asked Allah for?** I had asked Him for lots of things, obviously, 😊 but there was this one thing I wanted more than anything else, and I would find out soon.

*My Mum said Allah ALWAYS responds to our Dua, but because He knows what's best for us, sometimes He gives it to you in the next life, sometimes He stops something bad from happening to you instead, and other times He gives you exactly what you asked for!

Also, the Eid salah is DIFFERENT and I didn't really know what to do, so I copied my dad.
After the Eid salah and khutbah (the talk right after) everyone hugged each other and said,
'EID MUBARAK!' Even Aasiya and I hugged each

other, which we hardly ever do! Everyone looked really happy. My Mum said that's **exactly what Allah wants. He wants us to be happy on Eid.**

Just as one of my mum's friends released me from a **VERY SQUASHY HUG,**

I SAW HIM, AND I KNEW ALLAH HAD GIVEN ME WHAT I ASKED FOR.

It was my Dada, **my granddad!** He was here! **He was feeling better and had come out of the hospital in time for Eid.** I've never done an Eid

without my Dada! Aasiya and I hugged him as hard as I could without hurting him. Even Yusuf wrapped his arms around his leg.

"Taqabbal Allaahu minna wa minkum," Dada smiled.

"What does that mean?" I asked?

"It means, may Allaah accept (this worship) from us

and from you. Meaning all the worship you did during Ramadan," he replied.

"I like that! I'm going to say it to everyone!" Aasiya beamed.

We all went home for the big feast. Peggy had even brought over some more of her yummy brownies and the adults gave us AWESOME PRESENTS.

One of them was a new bike! **Alhamdulillah.** I felt so **HAPPY.** Ramadan had been the best month of the year. My parents were right, I did feel **stronger** and like **I HAD BECOME A BETTER ME.**

I reached for the **LAST BROWNIE** on the plate, but Aasiya came out of nowhere, picked it up and quickly *LICKED IT ALL OVER*. I felt like I was going to explode with anger, for a second, but instead, we both **GiGGLED UNTiL OUR TUMMiES HURT.**

JOURNAL PAGES BEGIN HERE.

Remember, this journal is YOURS. You can be real here. You don't have to show it to ANYONE. It's between you and ALLAH.

We're going to make the most of Ramadan because
we're smart.

RiGHT?!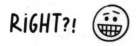

This is the chance to:

- get tremendous rewards!
- Be forgiven!
- And become a better, stronger, happier person!

INSHA'ALLAH!

Forgive!

Before Ramadan arrives, you should **make youʀ Heaʀt clean and tidy so tHat it's ʀeady to do gʀeat tHings!** Just the way we clean the house like crazy when guests are coming, so it's ready for them and for us to host them in the best way we can. If your heart isn't clean, if it has things like **GRUDGES** 😠 and **HATRED** in it, you won't be able to put many good things into it, because there **won't be any space!** If there's no space, you won't be able to get the most out of your good deeds in Ramadan, and you won't be able to grow into a **better you.**

SOOOO, even if Ramadan has already started, have a think about whether there's anyone you have bad feelings towards; someone you haven't forgiven. You can make up a **CODE NAME** for them and write it below. Then write that you are forgiving them, because who knows why they behaved the way they did. It doesn't mean you have to go and be best friends with them, or think that what they did was OK, but just forgive them in your heart so **your heart doesn't have to hold the pain in there anymore.**

When you forgive, it actually makes you feel lighter and happier! AND you get rewarded by Allah for forgiving people! **So, you win. COOL!**

I forgive _____

_____

_____

_____

_____

_____

_____

_____

_____

_____

_____

_____

_____

Be Forgiven!

You forgave people in your heart. Now have a think about anyone **you might have upset**, who might be holding bad feelings for YOU in their heart.
Insha'Allah nobody is, but just in case, have a think.

If you can think of anyone you've hurt, say sorry and ask them to forgive you. You can also ask **ALL** your family and friends to forgive you just in case, because even if you don't think you ever upset them, you might have done it without knowing.

GET CREATIVE! MAKE THEM A CARD, OR WRITE A LETTER, OR A FUNNY RHYME!

Otherwise, just give them a call, or send an email or message.

Your Ramadan good deeds list

Go back to the page where my mum tells me all the good deeds I can do. Think about which ones from the list you think you would be good at doing, or can do every day of Ramadan. Write them below. Next to each good deed, write down how much of it you want to do every day.

Remember, we are going to stick to this plan, so don't make it hard for yourself - plan to do what you actually will be able to do!

Batman

For example:

Good deed	How much
Reading Qur'an	Half a Quran a day.

I KNOW hardly anyone will actually do that, so don't aim for it. Aim for what you know you can do. It has to be quality over quantity.

Make your list and start doing what's on it every day, from today. There's a page you can **cut out and stick on your wall to keep track.** And I'll check in with you soon!

This list will get you to Jannah!

Good deed	How much

YOU CAN CUT THAT
PAGE OUT USING
SCISSORS.

YOU CAN ALSO RIP IT
OUT, BUT I THINK THAT'S
A SERIOUSLY BAD IDEA.

My good deed/Ibadah tracker

For each day, give yourself a star for each of the good deeds on your list. If you have five things on your list and you did them all, you give yourself five stars, if you only did two, you get two stars and if you did none, draw one circle.

Ramadan day 1	Ramadan day 2
Ramadan day 3	Ramadan day 4
Ramadan day 5	Ramadan day 6
Ramadan day 7	Ramadan day 8
Ramadan day 9	Ramadan day 10
Ramadan day 11	Ramadan day 12
Ramadan day 13	Ramadan day 14
Ramadan day 15	Ramadan day 16
Ramadan day 17	Ramadan day 18
Ramadan day 19	Ramadan day 20
Ramadan day 21	Ramadan day 22
Ramadan day 23	Ramadan day 24
Ramadan day 25	Ramadan day 26
Ramadan day 27	Ramadan day 28
Ramadan day 29	Ramadan day 30

LOOK INSIDE YOU!

This bit is going to be hard! 😐 And you're going to have to be **honest with yourself.** Remember, you don't have to show it to anyone, not even me, OK?

Think about **bad habits** that you have – the things you do that you know you shouldn't be doing. Things that you would change about yourself if you could. We all have habits like that because **none of us are perfect.** You saw in the book that sometimes I can be greedy, but Ramadan and fasting helped me work on that.

Make a list below of things about you that you would like to work on. It could be jealousy, being argumentative, lying, impatience, treating others badly, backbiting (talking about others behind their back in a way they wouldn't like), watching stuff you know you shouldn't, using bad language, cheating and so on.

_____   _____

_____   _____

_____   _____

_____   _____

_____   _____

_____   _____

_____   _____

Well done for being honest with yourself. You're cool! 😎

You thought about bad things you don't want to do, or ways you don't want to be. **NOW THINK OF WHAT YOU DO WANT TO BE!** 😇 What do you think a person that Allah loves is like? The person that gets to go to the highest level of Jannah – Jannatul Firduas.

Make a list of their characteristics. What is their behaviour like? What kinds of things do they do? How do they talk to people?

_____

_____

_____

_____

_____

_____

_____

_____

_____

_____

_____

_____

That's a list of how you will try your best to be during Ramadan. It'll be easy, because Shaytan can't whisper to you. Then you can carry on being that way after Ramadan too insha'Allah!

My mum says Allah never punishes a kid for doing something wrong, because they're just a kid, but the DANGER is that if you allow yourself to do wrong things as a kid, you get into the habit of it, and then it's super hard to change. So, WE HAVE TO TRAIN OURSELVES FROM NOW, NOT TO DO BAD THINGS, AND TO ASK FORGIVENESS IF WE DO.

Ramadan is our chance to be forgiven by Allah for any out of order things we might have done. Allah loves to forgive us, and He loves it when we turn to Him, even if we did something bad.

DO this:

Sit down in a **quiet place, alone,** if you can. Think about anything you have done which you aren't happy about and talk to Allah from the heart. Ask Him to forgive you for it. You can just ask in your own words, in any language, because that way, you will understand exactly what you're saying, and really mean it. But below are some duas that the prophets used:

"Rabbi'ghfir wa'rham wa anta khayrur-raahimeen (My Lord! Forgive and show mercy, for You are the Best of those who show mercy!)" [Surah al-Mu'minoon 23:118].

"Rabbanaa 'ghfar lanaa dhunoobanaa wa israafanaa fi amrinaa (Our Lord! Forgive us our sins and transgressions (in keeping our duties to You)." [Surah Aal 'Imraan 3:147].

This word means, overstepping.

'Allahumma anta rabbi la ilaaha illa anta, Khalaqtani wa ana 'abduka wa ana 'ala 'ahdika wa wa'dika ma astata't. A'oodhu bika min sharri ma sana'tu, aboo'u laka bi ni'matika 'alayya wa aboo'u laka bi dhanbi, faghfir li fa innahu laa yaghfiru'-dhunoob illaa anta (O Allah, You are my Lord. None has the right to be worshipped but You. You created me and I am Your slave, and I am faithful to my covenant and my promise (to You) as much as I can. I seek refuge with You from all the evil I have done. I acknowledge before You all the blessings You have bestowed upon me, and I confess to You all my sins. So I entreat You to forgive my sins, for nobody can forgive sins except You)."

Whoever says this during the day, having faith in it and dies before the evening comes, will be among the people of Paradise, and whoever says it during the night, having faith in it, and dies before the morning comes, will be among the people of Paradise." [Reported by al-Bukhaari, 5831].

Have You KepT A FAST Yet?
How did you feel? 😊

_____
_____
_____
_____
_____
_____
_____
_____
_____
_____
_____
_____
_____
_____
_____
_____
_____
_____
_____

INVITE SOMEONE FOR IFTAR.

Who's coming?

_____

_____

When are they coming?

_____

_____

What's on the menu?

_____

_____

_____

_____

_____

Plan to tell them something you learnt from this book. What will you tell them?

_____

_____

_____

_____

_____

_____

_____

I promised I'd check in with you on this...

Go back to your plan of good deeds to do during Ramadan and look at your tracker.

How are you doing with it?
Be honest!

I did read Qu'ran for 15 minutes every day, but I forgot to do dhikr for the last two days! I'll pull my socks up and start sticking to the plan better insha'Allah!

THE POWER OF DUA

Do you know that when we think of Allah, even just within our own mind, Allah mentions us to Himself too! Straight away. And in Surah al-Baqarah, Allah says **"And when my servants ask you about Me, I am near. I answer the call of every believer WHEN they call upon me.**

Exactly when we call Him! Do you see? 😁
Allah is keen and ready to listen to our duas, to listen to what we need. I mean, sometimes even our mums get fed up of us asking for stuff – food; help with homework; when we can have more screen time – but not Allah. He never gets tired of us when we want things from Him. Also, He is literally the ONE that has the power to give us what we want, but instead of asking Him, we worry our heads off and ask other humans to help us. That's so weird of us. 😉

So, this Ramadan, **make the BEST duas, starting today!** You'll be nuts not to!

Some PRO TIPS for dua making:

Start by praising Allah (say Alhamdulillahi rabbil'ala-meen) and sending salawaat (peace and blessings) on the prophet (saw).

Be aware that you really need Allah, and that He is the One who can help. Ask Him from that perspective. And then know that He is listening and will respond to you in the way that He knows best (He knows what you don't know).

Use some of Allah's names in your dua, according to what you're asking for (see the next activity).

Make sure you ask for great things in your next life, like Jannah and forgiveness, not only for things in this world.

I'm really excited for you to get everything you NEED with the **power of dua!**

DID YOU KNOW ALLAH HAS AT LEAST 99 NAMES?!

Do you know any of them? Write the ones you know, below. Then ask your adults for a book, or for them to teach you one or two names of Allah every day, with their meaning and how you can use the name. Then keep coming back and adding to your list!

_____

_____

_____

_____

_____

_____

_____

_____

_____

_____

_____

_____

_____

_____

_____

_____

_____

_____

_____

99 Names (continued)

_____
_____
_____
_____
_____
_____
_____
_____
_____
_____
_____
_____
_____
_____
_____
_____
_____
_____
_____
_____
_____
_____
_____
_____

LAYLATUL QADR IS COMMMMMMING!!!😧😃

You read what I wrote about Laylatul Qadr, so you know exactly why I'm so excited! And you know that **Laylatul Qadr – the Night of POWER** could be any of the odd nights of these last ten nights of Ramadan. **We have to look for it.** It's like a treasure hunt, because that night is actually a great treasure!

If you're awake that night, you might notice the stillness and peace that the night brings. And early in the morning, you can notice that the sun looks super soft and special. It doesn't give off sharp sun rays that make it hard to look at. Those signs are only way you can guess whether you found the treasure!

Do this:
Have a Laylatul Qadr treasure hunt with a group of friends. All of you look for the signs on the odd nights, make notes, and then on Eid day, you share which night you think Laylatul Qadr was on!

YOUR BODY IS AN AMANAH

– something Allah has given to you and asked you to take care of.

When we fast, it's really healthy for our bodies. But sometimes, in Ramadan we undo the good by eating and drinking lots of unhealthy things at iftar, like fizzy drinks and sweets.

It's OK to have a little bit of something as a treat on some days, but your **AIM** should be to feed your body foods that will make it healthy. You know what they are, right?

Make a list of your favourite Healthy foods.

_____

_____

_____

_____

_____

_____

Make this promise:

I promise to feed myself at least _____ portions of fruit and vegetables a day, and I promise to drink _____ glasses of water a day.

(Aim for 6–8 glasses a day!)

WE ARE BLESSED!

It's Ramadan, and whether you're fasting or not, you might have realised that you're **feeling more grateful** for some things in your life. I know that when I fasted, I was majorly grateful for water. Something as basic as water! 😮

What are you grateful for in your life?

_____

_____

_____

_____

_____

_____

_____

_____

_____

_____

_____

_____

_____

_____

_____

_____

_____

KINDNESS IS COOL 😎

Did you know that being kind is the only way to be?!
The Prophet (saw) said these things about being
kind and gentle:

'Allah is gentle and He loves gentleness. He rewards
for gentleness what is not granted for harshness and
He does not reward anything else like it.'
Sahih Muslim

'He who is deprived of kindness is deprived of
goodness.'
Sahih Muslim

So, imagine how much Allah LOVES people who
treat others kindly? And how much **REWARD** we
will get for being kind?!

Also, think about any time you've seen someone
behaving rudely and selfishly, literally nobody in the
room admired or wanted to be like that person,
right? Now think about when you saw someone
being **KIND** - maybe giving up their seat for an
elderly person on a train, or going easy on someone
who made a mistake – everyone admired that
person, right? *Everyone wanted to be like them.*
SO, kindness is cool!

Do this on the next page…

BRAINSTORM some ideas below about how you can be kind, then spend the day being as **kind** as possible. Notice how **others treat you,** then come back here and write down how your day was.

_____

_____

_____

_____

_____

_____

_____

_____

_____

_____

_____

_____

_____

_____

_____

_____

_____

_____

_____

_____

Do you Know ALLah?

Do you know Allah? How much do you know about what Allah is like? And what He does? If you had to explain to someone who Allah is, what would you say? Write it down below.

_____

_____

_____

_____

_____

_____

_____

_____

_____

_____

_____

_____

_____

_____

_____

If you found that you couldn't write much, ask your adult to study the meaning of **SURAH IKHLAS** in detail with you. Do it as a family. Trust me, you'll thank me! You'll also get to know Allah more and more if you do the 99 names activity!

CHARITY

The word for charity which you *GIVE BECAUSE YOU WANT TO, NOT BECAUSE YOU HAVE TO,* is 19-1-4-1-17-1-8

You have to decode it! It's in the A1Z26 code, where each letter of the alphabet is a number. A is 1, B is 2 and so on.

Decode it here _____.

Did you know, sadaqah doesn't have to be money. You can also give a smile, ☺ or a helping hand to someone who needs it. And if you do want to give something, you can give whatever you have – even half a date!

THE PROPHET (SAW) WAS THE MOST GENEROUS OF PEOPLE, AND HE WAS MOST GENEROUS DURING RAMADAN. He's the best man to ever live, and I want to be just like him if I can, so I've been trying to give, give, give!

Giving sadaqa **removes sins,** protects us from tough things happening in our lives, and brings more **blessings** to our lives. In fact, when you give sadaqah, Allah multiplies it for you and gives it back to you eventually!

HOW COOL IS THAT?

That means, **giving doesn't make you poorer. It makes you richer,** in your deeds and in how much wealth you have. When I found all that out, I was bursting to give charity. 😄

DO this: today, decide that **you** will become a more generous person. Decide that **you** will always look for people who need your smiles, help or money.

If you don't have any pocket money to donate, maybe you could do something that your parents are happy to pay you for, then you could donate some from that. I helped wash Dad's car for £5. The wheels were so dirty, the ground turned black when all the yucky stuff got washed off! 😮

By the way, there's a charity called **Zakaat** which adults have to give, if they have a certain amount of money. They have to give 2.5% of their money to needy people, every year. A lot of people give their Zakaat in Ramadan because the reward for giving is multiplied – it's more than in other months.

Kindness to animals

In a hadith in Bukhari, Abu Hurayrah (ra) quotes the Prophet (saw) as saying: "A man was walking, and he was very thirsty. He went down a well to drink. When he came up, he found a panting dog who was licking the earth because of his thirst. The man thought: This dog is as thirsty as I was a short while ago. He went down the well again, filled his shoe with water, and came up holding the shoe by his mouth. He gave it to the dog to drink. God appreciated that by forgiving him his sins. People asked the Prophet: Are we given a reward for kindness to animals? He said: You shall be rewarded for a kindness to any living thing."

You know I LOVE animals, so I was bouncing off the walls to hear this! It means whenever I'm taking care of my cat, CoCo, feeding her, stroking her, giving her water, I AM GETTING REWARDS! Dad said, even if I look after plants, I will be rewarded!

Do you have a pet? _____

Write about something kind you did for a living thing that wasn't a human!

_____

_____

_____

TAWAKKUL - YOUR SUPER POWER!

All through Ramadan, you've grown closer to Allah. So, we are ready to talk about **tawakkul** and how sweet it is!

Tawakkul means trusting in Allah. Really, actually trusting Him. It's almost like a super power, because if you Have tawakkul, you Handle tHings like a boss! You feel free of **WORRIES**, free of **FEAR** and like you're on top of the world!

When we don't have tawakkul, we panic and worry and end up not doing our tasks as excellently as we could have. Plus, Allah is in charge of literally everything. Imagine you were in charge of doing something and nobody trusted you would do it right? It's hurtful, right? Well, Allah says He is as we expect Him to be, so imagine how much of a bad move it is not to trust Him?!

To understand Tawakkul properly, **so you can have it,** you need to do this:
Go to www.muslimchildrensbooks.co.uk and sign up as a member of the site. **It's free!** On the members page, find the PDF called, 'Trust in Allah,' and read it.

REMEMBER I TOLD YOU THE BEST DUA FOR LAYLATUL QADR! AND NOW THAT YOU'RE BECOMING A PRO AT MAKING DUAS, ASK FOR WHATEVER YOU WANT AND NEED ON THE NIGHTS OF LAYTALTUL QADR.

DEALING WITH THINGS THAT MAKE US GRUMPY 😠

Do you know what can make us be horrible to people? **GRUMPINESS** – that's what. And do you know what sometimes makes us grumpy? It's when we are **not satisfied** with something in our lives. When we're not happy with the way things are going, because we wanted them to go another way.

This month, you and I are trying to become a better (= not grumpy) person and part of that is being alright with what is going on in our lives, if it's not in our control.

The other day, we were on the motorway going to pick my granddad up from the airport, and Dad missed the exit when we were only 5 mins away, which ADDED ANOTHER 37 MINS until we would get there. **It was so frustrating!!!** And Dad became super grumpy. So, **WE WERE ALL MISERABLE.** But then Mum reminded him that there's nothing we can do. And that **Allah chose for that to happen,** for a good reason. And we would only get there when Allah chooses. Poor granddad was waiting, but he wasn't upset we were late. And it wasn't the end of the world.

After that, Dad said, "I wasted half an hour feeling stressed and not accepting what was part of Allah's plan. 😔 I wouldn't have been grumpy if I just said, alhamdulillah and been grateful that I had a warm car, and my family was with me and that granddad was waiting inside the warm airport. And it didn't last forever – nothing hard ever does!" 😳

I realised something **HUGE** then. Being angry is not worth it! We're not going to be on this Earth forever. You know that, right? This world, this dunya, is just for a while, and if you ask any grandma or grandpa, they'll tell you, it goes crazy fast. Jannah is forever.

So, if there are **TOUGH THINGS IN THIS WORLD** that you've been through, or are going through, just hold onto Allah, leave it to Him and know that it won't last forever. Good times will always come again. As long as you have belief in Allah, **you are winning - big time!**

Here are some good things that come out of tough things!

 - Allah tests those He loves, to give a chance to grow and get closer to him AND get more rewards.

- Going through something tough, makes us strong.

- Going through difficult things makes us more grateful, e.g when you get sick, you realise how great it is to be NOT SICK.

DO THIS:

Write about the last time something happened, which **you weren't happy about.** How did you behave? How could you react differently now that you understand all this?

_____

_____

_____

_____

_____

_____

_____

_____

_____

_____

_____

_____

_____

_____

_____

_____

_____

_____

Your growth plan for after Ramadan

My dad said whoever gets this far in the journal is a **super brilliant little human** and they could only have gotten this far if Allah loves them. So, CONGRATULATIONS! :)

After doing all the journal pages, you might be thinking you've got lots to learn about Allah, the Qur'an and how we can live the best lives if we follow the instructions Allah sent us.

So, you're going to write down a plan. But here's **the fun part** – you're going to write it on your favourite box of chocolates, and you're going to open the chocolates when you've completed every-thing on the plan! (Make sure the chocolates have a long best before date).

Write down what you want to learn.

Here's my plan:
Memorise 10 surahs.
Learn at least 50 names of Allah.
Pray all my 5 salahs a day, every day.

That's it!

Are you a better
you, yet?

Check out Zanib Mian's mainstream titles, featuring relatable Muslim life, wherever you normally buy books!

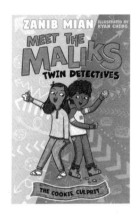

**Parents, follow us
@muslimchildrensbooks**